Cornish Engine Houses

Robert Hesketh and Paul White

GW00683423

Bossiney Books • Exeter

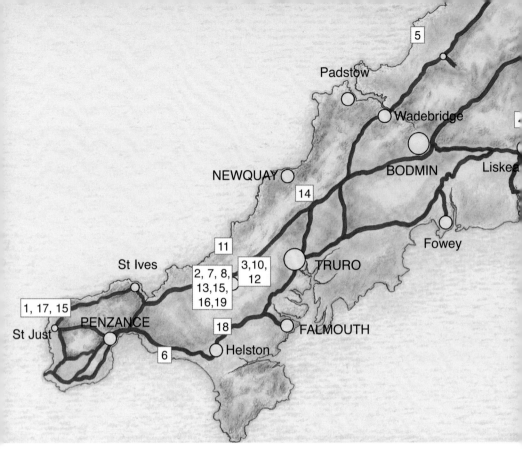

Approximate locations of the sites listed in this book

We have included both Ordnance Survey grid references and
What3Words references to help you locate places.

First published 2021 by
Bossiney Books Ltd, 68 Thorndale Courts, Whitycombe Way,
Exeter, EX4 2NY
www.bossineybooks.com

ISBN 978-1-906474-91-1

Acknowledgements
The map is by Graham Hallowell
All photographs are by Robert Hesketh, www.roberthesketh.co.uk
or from the publisher's own collection

Printed in Great Britain by Booths Print, Penryn

Introduction

Cornish engine houses are emblematic of Cornwall, but they house 'Cornish engines', which were exported across the world. There are some 200 engine houses surviving within Cornwall and just across the Tamar in West Devon, out of some 3000 said to have been constructed in the area, but they are now rare elsewhere in the UK.

Within Cornwall they are found in clusters, especially in West Penwith, around Camborne and Redruth, and near Minions on the south side of Bodmin Moor, with isolated examples elsewhere.

The aim of this book is to suggest attractive and interesting places to visit, and it only offers an introduction to engineering and mining history: there are many other books for those who get hooked!

The engine houses are of course mostly associated with tin and copper mining: the veins of these mineral ores extend along the granite outcrops from St Just in Penwith through Bodmin Moor to Dartmoor. On Dartmoor, perhaps surprisingly, there is just one engine house, though a very fine example called Wheal Betsy, north of Tavistock, see page 21.

At Wheal Betsy it was lead and silver which were mined rather than tin and copper. The mineral belt actually includes many metals, some of which were at times mined in Cornwall when they were in demand – zinc, arsenic and uranium for example – and in 2020 plans were announced for a lithium extraction plant to be built near Redruth, lithium being a key component of the batteries which are vital for a carbon-free future – but that extraction fortunately will not involve mining.

The tin mines up on Dartmoor lacked engine houses because they were able to depend on water power, which was far cheaper than shipping coal from South Wales around the Land's End. Even Wheal Betsy for many years depended on burning peat rather than coal, and the steam engine was probably used only a last resort when drought threatened the supply to the water-wheels.

Pumping was needed for other purposes than mining. A lonely engine house south of Tintagel (see page 18) drained the Prince of Wales quarry, as well as hauling slate up to the surface. At one time beam engines were sometimes used in clay pits to pump slurry – and London's waterworks used to depend on Cornish engines.

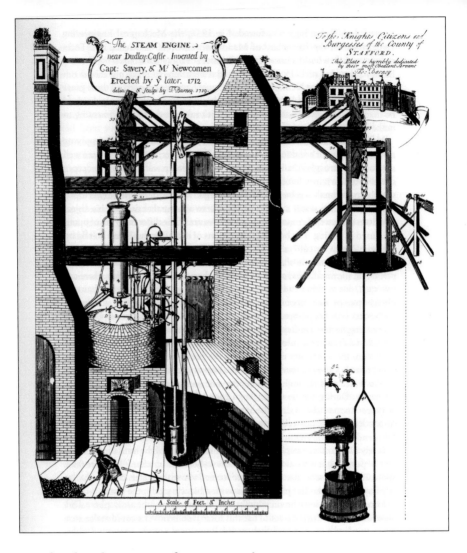

The STEAM ENGINE
near Dudley Castle. Invented by
Capt: Savery, & Mr Newcomen
Erected by ye later. 1712
delin: & sculp: by T. Barney. 1719.

To the Knights, Citizens and
Burgesses of the County of
STAFFORD.
This Plate is humbly dedicated
by their most Obedient Servant
Tho: Barney.

A Scale of Feet & Inches

The development of steam engines

The engine houses contained beam engines, most of which had a single function – either pumping water up out of the mine workings (a pumping engine) or hauling 'kibbles' of ore up the mine shaft, (a whim or winding engine) or, in tin workings but not copper, powering 'stamps' on the surface which broke up the ore. A few were ingeniously multi-purpose. A very small number helped the work-force up and down the shafts, but for the most part the miners were expected to climb ladders to reach the surface: accidents were frequent and miners had a low life expectancy.

4

Before steam engines were invented – and for a long time afterwards – water-wheels had been used to do the pumping, and also to power the stamps. Hauling up the kibbles was usually done by a horse-whim: a capstan was driven round by ponies which were whipped along by boys.

Thomas Newcomen (1664-1729) was an 'ironmonger' in Dartmouth who specialised in providing tools – copper and brass as well as iron – for the Cornish mines, and he was well aware that as the mines grew ever deeper the water power available in West Cornwall was often insufficient. The mines frequently had to resort to horse power.

Newcomen invented a 'fire engine', often called an atmospheric engine. This consisted of a piston inside a cylinder, on top of a boiler which in turn was on top of a furnace. All this was placed inside an engine house (see illustration opposite).

The piston was connected to a beam (in Cornish mines called a 'bob') which rested on the front wall ('bob wall') of the engine house, with its outer end connected to a rod which went down the shaft. Steam from the engine forced the piston down and the beam up, then the steam was released and the beam descended by force of gravity, driving the pumping system at the bottom of the shaft.

Newcomen was not alone in the venture: a Devon gentleman called Thomas Savery (c.1650-1715) had demonstrated a model steam engine to the Royal Society and to King William in 1699, and been granted a patent until 1733. Whilst his model worked well, the design became less efficient as the engine was scaled up: it could never drain a mine. So Newcomen, the non-conformist craftsman with a working engine, and Savery, the gentleman with the royal patent, joined forces.

Newcomen's engine was a huge improvement on horse-power, but it was by later standards inefficient in that it used a huge amount of coal, which in Cornwall had to be imported from South Wales. Coal cost five times as much by the time it reached a Cornish mine as it did at the pit-head. Whilst it is likely that the very first Newcomen engine was installed at Wheal Vor in 1710, most Cornish mines could not afford one. Newcomen's success came mainly in the Midland and Northern coal fields, where the engine's inefficiency was much less costly because there was coal on the spot.

Various attempts were made to improve the Newcomen engine, most successfully by the Yorkshireman John Smeaton who visited

Cornwall. Efficiency or 'duty' of steam engines was measured by the amount they could lift using a bushel of coal, in units of 'millions'. Early Newcomen engines had a duty under 4 millions, Smeaton raised this to 8 or 12 millions. But there was a limit, because of the Newcomen design, where the cylinder was alternately heated and cooled, wasting energy.

The breakthrough came when the Scottish engineer James Watt invented the first true steam engine in 1765, with a separate condenser. His business partner Matthew Boulton had excellent political and business connections, and Boulton & Watt were able to dominate the market until the end of the century, with a patent which was cleverly adapted to prevent any alternative designs.

As well as insisting on overseeing in detail the erection of their engines in Cornwall, Boulton & Watt charged the mine one third of the fuel savings they made. Since Watt's early engines had a duty of 25 millions, the saving was huge and the mine owners were at first delighted, and happy to pay it.

As time went by, however, the price of copper ore collapsed as a result of a plentiful and cheaper source being found on Anglesea, and various Cornish engineers came up with designs which were not based on Watt's, but which Boulton & Watt were nevertheless able to suppress. The mine owners and their engineers, such as Richard Trevithick and his father, fumed. The last decades ot the eighteenth century saw a number of court cases.

Once the Boulton & Watt patent expired, Trevithick invented what would become known as 'the Cornish engine' and because Trevithick spent all his energies inventing and did not bother much about business, he failed to protect himself adequately, with the result that improvements by other engineers were possible.

'Duty' now rose quickly. Trevithick's and Arthur Woolf's engines were at around 40 in the 1820s, but by the 1840s some engines achieved 80. Pumping engines became enormous, with cylinders as much as 2.3 metres (90 inches) in diameter.

The main difference from Watt's engines was that Cornish engines used high pressure steam, which risked explosions, so to be safe they required higher quality engineering to manufacture. Cornish engines were consequently very expensive to buy, and expensive to maintain compared to Watt's engines, and it only made sense to install them where coal was costly, as in Cornwall, or in London, where a Cornish engine was installed at the East London Waterworks in 1838.

The ups and downs of metal mining

Investing in Cornish mines was always a huge gamble by comparison with coal mining. The wealth created when the gamble paid off could be astonishing, but metal 'lodes' might be less than a metre wide so locating a lode was not easy, and was likely to be expensive. Even when a lode had been found, following it could be difficult. Many would-be mines came to nothing.

But an even greater hazard was the sudden discovery of a cheaper or better source elsewhere. Copper mining became hugely profitable in Cornwall in the 18th century, because of the increasing use of the alloy brass for taps and valves, both industrial and domestic, and also for the copper sheathing of wooden hulled ships. Then came the discovery of copper on Anglesea. From 1770 to 1800 the Cornish copper industry struggled, until supplies on Anglesea became exhausted. For a time Cornish copper flourished again, but in the 1830s copper was discovered in the USA and in Chile, at the same time as the lodes in west Cornwall were becoming harder to exploit.

Much the same happened with tin. A cheap source was discovered in Malaya in 1848, but at first piracy and local anarchy wrecked the Malayan trade: the price of tin rose to £153 a ton in 1870 and Cornwall was soon producing half the world's tin – but when order was restored in Malaya the price fell to £35 a ton. Mines closed.

Whereas coal is bulky and therefore expensive to transport, smelted tin or copper takes relatively little space and can be transported across the world. The price of coal in the 19th century was fairly stable, but the price of metals could vary wildly.

Add to this general situation the risks of problems at an individual mine – accidents, breakages, etc – and it is not surprising that many Cornish mines closed from time to time, sometimes reopening when the market improved, or a new lode was discovered.

Because the great beam engines were so expensive to install, there was a brisk second-hand market, both within Cornwall and beyond. At Prestonpans on the coast near Edinburgh a Cornish engine survives in excellent condition which was manufactured in 1853 at a Plymouth foundry and used in three different mines in Devon and

The Cornish engine at Prestongrange Museum, Prestonpans, near Edinburgh, which had served at three West Country mines before being renovated in 1873 and reconstructed in Scotland – where it worked draining a coal mine until 1954

Cornwall before being renovated by Harveys of Hayle in 1873; they provided it with a new beam and sold it to the Prestongrange Colliery where it was erected by Matthew Loam of Liskeard, in an engine house of local stone. Amazingly, it worked there until 1954. But the need to transfer it between three mines between 1853 and 1873 surely tells us something about the industry at that time.

The structure of engine houses

The primary function of a Cornish engine house was not to shelter the engine – though doubtless it slowed down rusting and other deterioration, and the operator ('driver') was certainly happier in the dry. What mattered was the front or 'bob' wall, on which the beam rested.

The beam alone could weigh 50 tonnes, so this wall needed to be strongly built, which in Cornwall was done with massive granite blocks. The other three walls were there as buttresses for the bob wall, which also had to resist the vibrations of the beam's movement. Each engine house was individually designed to fit its engine.

The cylinder was bolted to a specially laid floor, and the whole structure was deliberately weighty, again to absorb the stresses of the engine and to counter the weight of the plunger rods.

Outside the engine house, and usually immediately next to it, was the boiler house, with one of more boilers, and a chimney perhaps attached to both buildings. Where the engine house survives, the boiler house has often disappeared, demolished when the mine was abandoned so that its smaller building blocks could be re-used.

The pumping engine was built right next to the open shaft, so that the rods attached to the outer end of the beam could descend into it. If the same shaft was used for winding up kibbles of ore, there might be a second whim engine house close by, though sometimes the whim continued to be operated by other methods – horses or water power. Whim engines were smaller, and of a different design which was more efficient at stopping and starting than the pumping engine, and were attached to a flywheel and a winding operation.

At tin mines there might be yet a further engine house which powered the 'stamps', machinery which crushed the ore stone as the first stage of processing. Copper ore was taken elsewhere for processing, usually to South Wales, especially Swansea.

Outside Cornwall, horizontal engines began to replace beam engines for whims and stamps from about 1830, and later electric power took over from steam. Most of the surviving engine houses were built between 1840 and 1875.

The demise of the industry, and its heritage

By the 1870s the industry was struggling, facing major competitors around the world. At the same time, the Cornish mines had been so long exploited that the easy sources were running out; they had to go deeper and deeper, and the costs began to be prohibitive.

By 1880 the majority of mines had ceased working, and those that continued in operation found that water from the neighbouring mines, now closed down and undrained, added to their problems.

The last four decades of the 19th century saw a quarter of a million Cornish miners emigrating to new areas of mining opportunity such as Australia, South Africa, America, Brazil and Mexico. Many of them sent money back home to support families, but at the same time the Cornish economy altered too: foundries such as Harveys of Hayle and Holman Brothers of Camborne changed the emphasis of their marketing to provide equipment – including Cornish beam engines –

for the new mining areas. Apparently there are twelve Cornish engine house sites in the Australian state of Victoria alone. Harvey's foundry survived until 1903, Holman Brothers until 1968. And the Camborne School of Mines continues to offer technical education to the world.

A few mines in Cornwall managed to survive into the 20th century. One which closed, and then reopened in 1899, was South Crofty, at Pool. It was able to extend its operations into neighbouring mine setts which remained closed, and the mine steadily modernised. It continued moderately profitably until 1985, when the international tin price collapsed. With some government support and by selling surplus land, the mine struggled on until 1998, when it closed, the last tin mine in Europe. However, strenuous efforts to reopen it soon started, and at the time of writing are still continuing, though the future is very uncertain.

In 2006 the 'Cornwall and West Devon Mining Landscape' was made a World Heritage Site by UNESCO, consisting of ten separate areas. UNESCO's attitude to reworking at South Crofty has yet to be decided. In the local population too, there is inevitably a division between those who are proud of their past, and wish to preserve reminders of it, and those who are proud of their past, and also wish to extend mining into the future.

Cornwall's engine houses perhaps survived in greater numbers than elsewhere because there has been little demand to re-use the old mining landscape, except for housing developments in a few towns, whereas at coal mining sites in the early twentieth century buildings were torn down to be replaced by new technology such as electric pumping.

So they may have survived by chance, but it is now clear that the engine houses are treasured both by Cornish people and visitors as a vital part of Cornwall's history.

Please remember that industrial sites can be hazardous and take due care, especially if you are accompanied by children or dogs. Tread carefully: although many shafts and pits have been fenced off there are sudden drops and much uneven ground. Loose rocks and debris are a potential hazard too, as is mine waste, which often contains traces of arsenic, a highly toxic substance.

Exploring engine houses

We here suggest visits to several well preserved and dramatically situated engine houses which are just a short stroll from a car park, and a number of heritage centres to visit, some with an entrance fee. But we start with two walks which each pass several engine houses.

The Great Flat Lode Walk

This scenic walk/cycleway circuits Carn Brea. It is well signed and surfaced and may be taken as a whole (11.7 km/7 1/4 miles), or in shorter sections. Of particular historic interest are South Wheal Frances (page 20) and the King Edward Mine Museum (page 27).

The area around Carnkie and Piece south of Carn Brea was intensively exploited for copper and tin between the early 18th and early 20th centuries, as its many ruined engine houses and mine buildings testify. This is recognized as one of the world's best preserved historic mining landscapes and can be explored on foot by following the Great Flat Lode Walk, so named after the enormous vein ('lode') of tin exploited here. The lode was unusual in running only 30° below the surface, whereas most lodes dived steeply underground at around 70°, necessitating deeper and deeper workings. The Great Flat Lode yielded 90,000 tons of high quality tin concentrate and employed thousands of men, women and children from the 1870s to the First World War.

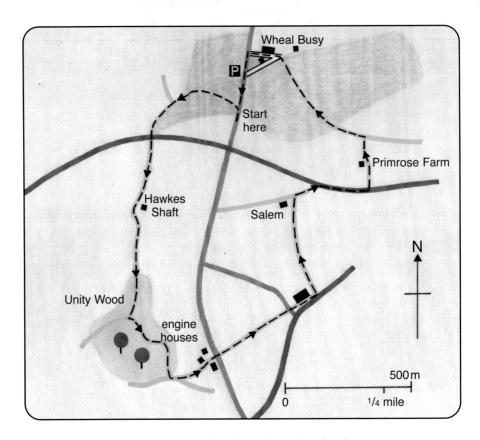

Killifreth, Unity Wood, Wheal Bush and Wheal Busy

Distance: 4 km (2 1/2 miles)

To get there, drive along the lane signed WHEAL BUSY off the Scorrier/Chacewater road. Start from the parking area by the first mine chimney. SW 738446 *///records.post.alleyway*

With your back to the chimney, turn right and walk only 30 m up the lane. Turn left and follow the rough path through heather to a path junction. Turn left and continue to a track junction.

Walk ahead to the road. Cross and take the track ahead, DEVORAN. Go through a gate, where a signboard explains the industrial history of the area. Continue to Hawke's Shaft Engine House (see page 13) with its wheelpit and lofty chimneystack. Follow the track ahead.

Enter Unity Wood. Ignore the path left here and continue ahead. When the track forks, keep left. Fork left at the next path junction.

Leave the wood and turn left into the track, DEVORAN. Only 20 m

12

Hawkes Shaft. For further details see page16.

If you don't want to do the full walk, Hawke's Shaft is just a five minute walk from the small parking area at SW734444 on the south side of the Chacewater/Scorrier road, 300 m before the Wheal Busy turning.
Look out for two stone markers inscribed 'Killifreth Mine' and 'Devoran' respectively

ahead, the track divides. Keep left. Cross the lane by Wheal Bush Cottage. On your left are two fine engine houses (Wheal Unity Wood, see page 23) which are best seen by diverting 100 m left up the lane. Having viewed them, return to Wheal Bush Cottage and turn left, PUBLIC BRIDLEWAY.

Cross the lane at Cox Hill and continue ahead, PUBLIC BRIDLEWAY. Turn left (PUBLIC BYWAY) at the junction with the road. Reaching Salem, turn right and continue to the road. Turn right and follow the road with care for 200 m.

Turn left, PUBLIC BRIDLEWAY. Continue uphill from Primrose Farm to a path junction and turn left. Follow the track ahead. Reaching the parking area by Wheal Busy (page 22) bear left. Continue to the lane. Turn left and continue to the start.

BOTALLACK MINE

1 Botallack and the Crowns engine houses

A host of atmospheric mine ruins remain on the coast between Botallack and Pendeen to commemorate the proud history of Cornish miners and their hard, skilled labour in difficult and dangerous conditions. The area was intensively mined until well into the 20th century and forms part of UNESCO's World Heritage Site covering Cornwall and West Devon's Mining Landscape.

An excellent place to start exploring is from the former Count House at Botallack Mine. Turn right out of the car park and walk past the metal headgear. Turn left onto the Coast Path, which passes several ruined buildings, including chimneys and calciners. Below are the iconic Crowns Engine Houses (see cover photo).

Perched half way down the cliff, they served Boscawen mineshaft. This descended diagonally at 32.5° beneath the restless sea and 800m (1/2 mile) from shore to a depth of 250 fathoms (455m). Miners could hear the sea booming overhead. The lower pumping house on Crowns cliff was built in 1835. It weighs 1200 tonnes and has no foundations – it is bolted and mortared into place on the rocks. Above this is the winder for the Boscawen shaft, constructed about 1860.

Car park: SW365333   ///wizards.view.roost

The Victorian print opposite was bought in Penzance by a Scottish lady visiting Cornwall in 1866, when the Crowns engine houses at Botallack were already a tourist attraction. Queen Victoria herself had visited in 1846, and the Prince and Princess of Wales actually descended the diagonal shaft under the sea in 1865. Poor profits, and then flooding, closed the mine in 1895, though there was an unsuccessful attempt to reopen in 1907.

2 Dolcoath Mine, Redruth

Dolcoath's New East Shaft winding engine house and South Harriet Shaft engine house, which accommodated a 60 inch pumping engine (later re-engineered to 65 inches) and built in 1860 by Perran Foundry, can be seen between Redruth and Camborne. A mine boiler and winding engine drums stand in front of South Harriet Shaft.

Dolcoath was a tin and copper mine known as 'The Queen of Cornish Mines'. It became the largest and deepest mine in Cornwall, producing an estimated 80,000 to 100,000 tons of black tin plus 350,000 tons of copper between the early 18th and early 20th centuries. It eventually reached a depth of 1000m (3300ft). Working at great depth burdened miners with a journey to and from the surface that took up to two/three hours each way and also produced hot and humid conditions in which the tropical scourge of hookworm thrived, causing 'miner's anaemia'.

South Harriet Shaft at Dolcoath

Working at great depths also called for a great deal of power. At the principal shaft, New Sump Shaft, the original engine with a massive 1.9m (76 inch) diameter cylinder was replaced with an even bigger engine with a 2.2m (85 inch) cylinder. This was so large that the engine house could not accommodate the stairs and a unique exterior wooden staircase was added. Dolcoath's various workings covered a large area.

Park near the intersection between Kerrier Way and Dolcoath Road (TR14 8RT). There is a small car park by New East Shaft, whilst South Harriet is a short walk along Kerrier Way in the Camborne direction.

3 Hawke's Shaft engine house, Killifreth Mine

Hawke's Shaft engine house has Cornwall's tallest surviving chimney-stack. It was built in 1891 to house an 80 inch diameter engine, but the stack was doubled in height for its final phase of operation from 1912 to 1924 to create extra draught for its four boilers. These served the new, more powerful 85 inch (216cm) cylinder engine.

Like many Cornish mines, Killifreth had mixed fortunes, largely dictated by volatile mineral prices. It was worked for copper from 1826 to 1860, then for tin until prices collapsed, forcing closure in 1897. In its final phase, Killifreth produced arsenic, but again a price slump forced closure.

4 Minions and Caradon

The Minions and Caradon area was the focal point for 4000 miners in its Victorian boom years and is littered with stark reminders of Cornwall's mining industries. Two of its most impressive engine houses are a short walk from the car park at the north end of Minions. SX262713   ///novelists.warns.pacifist

Houseman's engine house SX261715   ///during.possibly.dentistry

Dating from the mid-19th century, Houseman's engine house at South Phoenix Mine is built of granite rubble with granite quoins and brick dressings. South Phoenix was re-started for copper mining in 1847 and equipped with a 71cm (28 inch) rotary engine, going down to 120 fathoms (218m) by 1854. After the first few years it appears not to have been financially successful, but the success of Phoenix United to the north encouraged further exploration. Located 100m

Houseman's (left) and the Prince of Wales engine houses

north of the car park, Houseman's has been restored as the Minions Heritage Centre and is normally open all year with free admission. Well-illustrated tableaux explain in brief the industrial history of Minions, from early tin streaming to late deep mining, as well as the area's remarkable geology, prehistory, farming and quarrying.

Prince of Wales engine house   SX265723 ///crawling.solving.binds

A 750m walk north from the car park along the Henwood lane and right along a track leads to the Prince of Wales engine house, and associated buildings which housed a Robey two-speed horizontal winding engine and a six-head of pneumatic stamps. Used for tin workings from 1907-14, the engine house accommodated a 203cm (80 inch) diameter engine. One of the last really big Cornish engines, this was built in Camborne by Holman Brothers and was officially started by the then Prince of Wales (later George V) in 1909. It finally reached a depth of 200 fathoms (364m), but was a financial disaster, only producing 95 tons of black tin over seven years.

South Caradon Mine

There are very extensive remains of engine houses, dressing floors, mineral dumps and related structures in the Seaton valley between Crow's Nest and Minions and eastwards on the southern flank of Caradon Hill towards the parking area at Tokenbury Corner.

This is a classic mining boom and bust story. There had been tin streaming at Gonamena since at least 1662, but there were no mines around the hill. Then in 1833 a Captain Clymo and his son dug an adit (drain) into the side of the hill and discovered lodes of copper. His South Caradon Mine became the richest in Cornwall, totally changing the area overnight, with shanty towns 'resembling in character the mining camps of Colorado and the Far West'. Soon more mines opened – but in the 1870s the price of copper plunged; all the mines had been forced to close by 1888.

To explore the area, follow the broad track westwards from the parking area, past tips and mine ruins, to visit the well preserved engine house at Jope's Shaft which housed a 152 cm (60 inch) pumping engine built in 1855. Its three piece granite bedstone is still in place. Opposite Jope's shaft are the extensive Gonamena workings.

Park at Tokenbury Corner SX696280   ///fuzzy.spreading.lion

5 Prince of Wales engine house, near Trebarwith Strand

The Prince of Wales engine house is exceptional in serving a quarry rather than a mine. Replacing an earlier system of water power provided by a leat and waterwheel, it was installed in 1871 at a cost of £1590 to house a Woolf Compound Beam Engine which both hauled stone with an aerial ropeway and pumped water from the quarry. By 1880 the site was abandoned, but in 2015 the restored ruin of the engine house was auctioned for £81,000.

Follow the stepped path from SX071862 *///optimally.positive.adventure*

6 Rinsey: Wheal Prosper and Wheal Trewavas

Wheal Prosper is a 200m walk east from the National Trust car park at Rinsey and Wheal Trewavas another 1km east along the Coastpath. Wheal Prosper's name turned out to be ironical: it closed after six years' working in 1866. However, it gained posthumous fame as a setting for BBC TV's *Poldark*.

Rinsey car park: SW592271   ///races.kinder.tungsten

Wheal Prosper near Rinsey

Wheal Trewavas exploited copper from four lodes and employed around 160 men with workings that extended under the sea. There are two engine houses: Old Engine Shaft was built in 1834 and housed an 18 inch diameter engine to drain the mine. New Engine Shaft began work in 1836 with a 45 inch diameter engine. Although they raised 17,800 tons of copper they were eventually abandoned because of flooding, a major problem in many Cornish mines, but especially in those like Crowns at Botallack (page 14) that extended under the sea and mines built in valley bottoms like East Wheal Rose (page 25).

7 South Crofty, Pool

South Crofty was the final tin mine to close in Cornwall in 1998, bringing 4000 years of Cornish tinning to a close. However, at the time of writing (2021) the prospects of South Crofty re-opening are promising, pending further exploration and drilling. The development of new technologies has raised the demand for, and the price of, a range of minerals, including the tin, lithium and copper which still lie under Cornish ground. Cornish Metals, which owns South Crofty, holds mineral rights to over 15,000 hectares throughout Cornwall. It also has a mining licence valid until 2071 and is exploring other former mining sites for possible development, including Great Wheal Vor near Helston. Also exploring and hoping to develop Cornwall's huge mineral potential is rival firm British Lithium, based at Roche near St Austell. See page 31 for a photo of the South Crofty site.

Park at nearby Heartlands (page 32) to view the impressive metal headgear of New Cook's Engine Shaft at South Crofty from the outside.

8 South Wheal Frances

Some of the most extensive and impressive mine ruins on the Great Flat Lode Walk (page 11) are at the start, by South Wheal Frances car park, just south of Higher Carnkie. The first complex of buildings includes an engine house that accommodated a 101 cm (40 inch) and a 203 cm (80 inch) pumping engines and the winding engine house from the 1890s, which sheltered a horizontal engine made by the famous firm of Holman's at Camborne. Next to it is the boiler house, which contained six Lancashire boilers to power a pumping engine, winder, compressor, crusher and capstan. Take your time to explore the site and use the map at the far side to orient yourself. A five minute walk beyond it are two more impressive engine houses: Pascoe's winding engine house and Pascoe's pumping engine house (photo opposite). The latter housed an 80 inch engine built in 1887.

Car park: TR16 6JX   ///exchanges.comically.apple

9 Wheal Betsy

This engine house (photo below) is the only one to survive on Dartmoor, a prominent landmark on the east side of the A386 Tavistock to Okehampton road, just north of Mary Tavy. There are small parking places nearby. Alternatively, park carefully in Mary Tavy and take footpaths and lanes to the site.

Wheal Betsy was mainly a lead and silver mine, though copper and arsenic were also found. The mine had been worked since 1806, and probably long before that, but the engine house was only built in 1868 to house a Cornish beam pumping engine, and the mine closed in 1877. If viewed from the east, the chimney can be seen to be strangely curved.

Parking: SX 509814   ///twilight.deal.covertly

Wheal Bush   See Wheal Unity Wood

The engine house at Wheal Busy, built in 1856, which housed three different engines over the years

10 Wheal Busy

This was worked for tin in the 17th century; the 'adventurers' were keen on new inventions, and had a series of atmospheric and steam engines. At times, the name 'Wheal Busy' also covered Killifreth and Wheal Unity Wood. The engine house was built in 1856, and housed three different engines over the years, until work ceased in 1924.

11 Wheal Coates

One of West Cornwall's best preserved mining complexes, Wheal Coates is highly evocative of the county's rich industrial heritage. The walk from the National Trust car park to the main site is short and relatively easy. However, some care is needed on the path down to Towanroath Engine House, which stands proudly on the cliff edge and pumped water from a 180 m (600 ft) deep shaft, allowing men to mine tin beneath the sea. There are also two whim (winding) engine houses, which crushed ore for smelting, a chimney, a stamps house and a calciner for burning off impurities, including arsenic. The present mine opened in 1802, but records show mining began here in 1692 – in good time to be an authentic setting for BBC's *Poldark*.

Car park: SW703500   ///aspect.hourglass.peach

Towanroath engine house at Wheal Coates

12 Wheal Unity Wood

This is said to have been worked from the 16th century, and was formerly known as Wheal Bush. It was a successful copper mine in the first half of the 19th century, then worked off and on till 1903. Our walk (see page 12) passes a surviving pair of engine houses, but surprisingly the mine extended right through the wood.

Engine houses at Wheal Unity Wood, formerly known as Wheal Bush

Left: Mitchell's Shaft at East Pool Mine
Right: East Wheal Rose engine house, at the Lappa Valley Railway

Museums and visitor attractions

N.B. Please check opening times before visiting.

13 East Pool Mine

East Pool Mine was worked from the early 18th century until 1945, first for copper and later for tin. It has two preserved steam engines on separate sites, a winding engine at Mitchell's Shaft and a pumping engine at Taylor's Shaft, both owned by the National Trust.

Mitchell's Shaft houses an engine with a 76cm (30 inch) cylinder running at 17 revolutions per minute. The bob weighs 8½ tons. Designed by local engineer E W Mitchell, the engine was built by

Holman's of Camborne in 1887 and was the last rotative beam engine made in Cornwall. Mitchell's worked until 1921, when a large underground movement of rock destroyed the mine.

Taylor's Shaft was sunk in 1922 and the 1892 Harvey's engine, previously at Carn Brea Mine, was installed in 1924. Its massive 90 inch engine has a 52 ton bob and a correspondingly solid six foot thick bob wall in the engine house to support it. Running at five strokes per minute, it was powered by five Cornish boilers. It generated 400 HP and raised 90 gallons of water on each stroke. Although Taylor's Shaft was closed in 1945, the engine continued to pump at South Crofty (page 20) until replaced by electric pumps in 1954.

The highly informative tour at Taylor's Shaft begins with an explanation of the mine's history and the purpose of the various buildings. It continues with an explanation of how the machinery worked with the aid of various models and a wide range of mining artefacts. A video using archive footage gives a potted history of Cornish mining. The tour continues with a visit to the engine house.

Mitchell's Shaft was closed at the time of writing, though it is hoped to re-open and have the engine in action again in the future.

14 East Wheal Rose

Visitors to the Lappa Valley Railway can view East Wheal Rose silver and lead mine. It has Cornwall's largest remaining engine house, built in 1881 to house a massive engine to pump this notoriously wet mine, scene of a terrible disaster in 1846 when flash flooding drowned 39 miners. The engine's cylinder was 100 inches (2.5m) in diameter. Installing it was a major task, as the beam section alone weighted 46 tons, the cylinder bottom a further 13 1/2 tons and its cover a further 8 1/4 tons, while the newly cast beam was 56 tons. Both engine and beam were built by the world renowned Cornish engineering firm, Harvey's of Hayle.

The nearby chimney was built apart from the engine house because the ground was soft and its weight might have caused the engine house to tilt. At 36 m (120 ft) it is unusually tall, but this height enabled it to give the strong draught needed for the boilers to produce sufficient steam for the engine.

Car park: SW 838 573   ///woods.warrior.twee

A view of Geevor Mine: it closed as recently as 1990, and from a distance the surviving buildings look more like a coal mine of that period, with no surviving engine house

15 Geevor Mine, Trewellard

Hard rock mining continued at Geevor Mine until 1990. Preserved as a monument to Cornwall's industrial history, Geevor gives a vivid impression of what hard rock mining was like. As well as the various mine buildings and their machinery, there are many well-preserved artefacts, period photographs, archive films and interactive exhibits, plus an underground tour, usually conducted by a former Geevor miner. Most memorable of all is the miner's 'dry', the changing rooms where the men gathered for work, exchanged banter and showered off the red grime from their tired bodies at the end of a shift. Their helmets, boots and clothes stand by their open lockers, on one of which a man has sprayed in large, block letters 'THE END 16/2/90'. All around the walls are large black and white full face portraits of Geevor miners.

The self-guided tour begins with a museum outlining the history of Cornish tin mines with period photographs. A mine model shows how Geevor, Botallack and Levant form a complex of mines, with 90 shafts and 100 miles of tunnels, which extended to a maximum depth of 640 m (2100 ft) and almost one mile under the sea at Levant.

Next stop is the Compressor House, where three large machines produced compressed air to power rock drills, shovels, winches and fans in the mine. The Winder House follows, with both the old steam winder and the 1954 electric winder.

Visitors move on through the Mine Rescue room and Drill Shop to the Hard Rock Museum, which gives a very good historical perspective, whilst working models further demonstrate the industrial process. Using rare archive footage and interviews, the cinema explains the tin mining process and the eventual closure (despite a vigorous campaign of protests) of Geevor.

16 King Edward Mine

There are two engine houses at the fascinating King Edward Mine Museum, Troon, Camborne. Standing next to the Great Flat Lode Walk (page 11), the South Condurrow Stamps House was erected in 1869 and drove 48 heads of stamps – heavy weights lifted and dropped (by either water or steam power) to pulverize the tin bearing rock to a fine sand, thus releasing the tin mineral.

Next to it, a small shaft was sunk to draw water from a deep adit for ore dressing.

The second engine house is within the museum grounds. Built in 1868, it was for a 25 inch beam winder engine. Originally, it wound from a shaft across the field to the west, but later was used to wind from two shafts, one to the north and one to the south. In the yard next to it is a boiler manufactured by Visick's Foundry in Perranarworthal about 1890.

The excellent guided tour of King Edward Mine gives a comprehensive potted history of Cornish mining and engineering, aided by

King Edward Mine, the South Condurrow Stamps House, erected in 1869

a wide range of mining machinery and explanatory plaques. Much of the machinery was made locally by Harvey's of Hayle and Holman's of Camborne. Of particular interest is the steam winder bought from Holman's in 1908 to hoist from the 400 ft (122 m) deep engine shaft on site. It is the only Holman winder to survive in the UK and replaced the older beam winder whose engine house stands by the extensive museum.

King Edward Mine itself was originally called South Condurrow Mine, before shutting in 1895. Taken over by the world famous Camborne School of Mines, it was used to train students in a wide range of skills and became the most photographed mine in Cornwall. Many of the superb archive mining photographs on the Royal Cornwall Museum's website were taken at King Edward Mine in the late 19th/early 20th century.

Levant Mine, with the boiler house in front of the whim building and the pump engine house to the right

17 Levant Mine

Levant Mine in Trewellard is cared for by the National Trust and open to the public. Levant includes a boiler house, a whim building and a pump engine house. Its 1840 engine built by Harvey's of Hayle has been restored to working order – the only steam driven Cornish beam engine operating on its original site. The Levant complex extends over a wide area and incudes many chimneys and ruined mine buildings, which may be explored from the Coast Path and adjoining tracks and public footpaths.

There is great poignancy about Cornwall's ruined mines, especially Levant, which was the scene of a tragic accident in 1919. Many miners had served in the Great War and it had been hard to keep up the usual standard of maintenance during those four years. Thirty two miners were killed and many more injured when the metal rods supporting the man engine carrying miners to and from the deep workings broke and plunged down the shaft.

SW368346   ///fattening.mopped.lied

18 Poldark Mine, Trenear, Helston

Poldark Mine's 1846 Cornish beam engine has a 76 cm (30 inch) cast iron cylinder and its 12 ton bob rests on a stout bob wall of reinforced concrete blocks. As it is not now within an engine house, it offers an unusually complete view of a steam engine. Built by Harvey's of Hayle, it was moved here from the Bunny Tin Mine near St Austell and was worked until 1959, the last commercially operated engine in Cornwall.

Originally called Wheal Roots, Poldark Mine is in the Wendron Mining District where ores have been extracted since prehistoric times. Although tin mining ceased here about 1800, water powered tin stamps and dressing floors, which had been worked since the 13th century, continued operations until the 1870s. This long history is set within the context of Cornwall's ancient mining story for visitors, who are taken on underground tours of three stopes by knowledgeable guides. Allow additional time to explore the six acre site, which has a host of mining artefacts and the large and eclectic Cornish Heritage Collection in the Museum.

Poldark Mine was closed for renovation at the time of writing (2021), but it is hoped it will re-open in 2022.

The centre of South Crofty mine seen from the Great Flat Lode Walk

Robinson's Shaft at Heartlands, part of South Crofty Mine

19 Robinson's Shaft, Heartlands Redruth

As well as its excellent museum with free entry, Heartlands, the Cornish mining world heritage site in Redruth, offers guided tours of Robinson's Engine House with its 1854 Cornish pumping engine.

Robinson's Shaft was part of Cornwall's last working mine, South Crofty (page 20), which closed in 1996. Its engine has an 80 inch cylinder and a 38 ton bob. It worked at 5 strokes per minute and pumped water at depths of over 600m at a rate of 310 gallons per minute. Robinson's was also the last Cornish engine to work in a Cornish mine. It finally stopped in 1955 after 52 years at Robinson's, a tribute to its design by Captain Samuel Grose, a pupil of Richard Trevithick, and its building at the Copperhouse Foundry in Hayle by Sandys, Vivian & Co. It was first erected at Wheal Alfred near Hayle and worked there from 1855 to 1862. Later it was moved to Wheal Abraham near Crowan (1865-75) and subsequently to Tregurtha Downs near Marazion.

Heartlands' extensive and recently refurbished museum tells the story of Cornwall's 'Great Migration' with the aid of maps and historic and modern illustrations. Half a million Cornish people migrated in the 19th and early 20th centuries to seek a new life. Many were mineworkers and engineers, who took their skills to the mines of Australia, South Africa and America.

SW668412 ///logo.firebird.free

The Newcomen Memorial Engine at Dartmouth Visitor Centre

Dartmouth's Visitor Centre houses the world's oldest preserved steam engine, where it can be seen in motion (though now electrically operated). It was designed and installed by Thomas Newcomen (1664-1729), see page 5.

This Newcomen engine was moved and rebuilt several times, last serving at Hawkesbury Junction in Warwickshire, where it pumped water into a canal until 1913. It was reassembled in Dartmouth in 1964 on the 300th anniversary of Newcomen's birth.